SUNDIATA

■ ■ ■ ■ ■ ■ ■ ■

the epic of the Lion King

SUNDIATA

■ ■ ■ ■ ■ ■ ■ ■ ■

the epic of the Lion King

retold by Roland Bertol
Illustrated by Gregorio Prestopino

THOMAS Y. CROWELL COMPANY ■ NEW YORK

DESIGNED BY TONI KRASS

MANUFACTURED IN THE UNITED STATES OF AMERICA

L.C. CARD 75–81945

I 2 3 4 5 6 7 8 9 10

To Diane Bass, Who Is a
First-Class Sorceress

Introduction

When I came back to Paris from North Africa, everything looked dull and grim. A few of us met in a café. Mamadou, born near Bamako in Mali, was sipping mint tea and talking about his father's rifle.

". . . Then when I was twelve my father said it was time for me to show I was a man. He gave me that old rifle and one bullet. That night I had to walk alone through roadless brushland to the next village. The bullet was for an emergency."

The Norwegian asked, "What if there were more than one emergency?"

"Eh bien, *the bullet was for the most serious emergency.*"

"*But how could you tell which was the most serious one?*" *Norwegians are practical people.*

Mamadou sipped his tea. "Afterwards," he answered. Malians are subtle people.

Africa is a subtle land. Some of its ideas are like those of the West, some are different; all are meaningful. Africa has always been a land of great empires and wisdom, and the West is beginning to learn this is so.

* * * * *

Sundiata was born in the early part of the thirteenth century. He built a kingdom which straddled the great trading routes connecting North Africa and Black Africa. Mali quickly grew into a powerful trading empire. In exchange for such things as dry goods and books, the Arabs took gold and other products. Mansa Mussa, a later emperor of Mali, made the pilgrimage to Mecca with a retinue of several thousand men. Nearly one hundred camels were needed to carry the ten million dollars in gold which he brought along to pay for expenses. The Arabs were stunned by that show of wealth, but it was the cultural and intellectual wealth of Mali which the Arabs admired.

While Europe struggled through the barbarism of the Dark and Middle Ages, Arab scholars preserved the works of Aristotle and much of classical civilization. And that same brilliant Arab scholarship praised the universities of Mali. For a time, Timbuktu was a famous center of trade and learning. It was one of Mali's proudest cities.

Mali began to decline with the coming of the European to Africa. But it is wrong to blame slavery or colonialism for the decay of Mali. When Europe opened sea routes to Africa, the camel caravans became too costly and too slow. The landlocked empire of Mali died a natural death. Today Timbuktu is a choking desert town of few people and of ruined houses crumbling slowly back into sand.

Bilali, saheb—companion—of Muhammad and the first muezzin of Islam, was the ancestor of the Keita family, to which Sundiata belonged. The influence of Islam has always been a part of Mali, but Africa remains African in spite of Arab and European influences. In the Sundiata legend the God of Islam shares His divinity with the spirits of earth, water, and sky, for these things are bound together in holiness and sacredness.

Owing to the lack of a written language, the legend of Sundiata has been passed on by word of mouth for some seven hundred years. The creative art of the storyteller, or griot, slowly transformed historical fact into an epic blending history with myth. Because the epic is meant to be recited in marketplaces, I tried to capture some of the feeling of an inflected language with the style I used.

There are dozens of versions of the Sundiata legend, depending upon regional and cultural differences. I selected what I felt were the most interesting elements from the wide choice I had and put them together. Sometimes I suppressed long episodes which, although beautiful, wandered away from the main thrust of the epic.

I have relied upon several thirteenth-century Arab texts; upon unpublished manuscripts, plays, and fragments which my Malian friends gave me; and to a lesser extent upon published fragments and a recent French translation by D. T. Niani of the epic as told in the town of Djeliba Koro. Carolyn Swetland, a tireless Africanist associated with the University of Oslo, and Ralph Thorslund, whose knowledge of Islamic culture and Arabic is endless, have helped me very much.

SUNDIATA

■ ■ ■ ■ ■ ■ ■

the epic of the Lion King

Prologue

It is the dry season. The sun burns the plains until the grass is brown, and when a lion roars at night his voice is like the dry cough of old men. Outside the town of M'Baykoro is a dead tree. The people of M'Baykoro call it the Vulture Tree because that is where the vultures wait. Today, the vultures do not stir. They hang from the branches like strange, black fruit.

Mamadou leans against the split-rail fence at the edge of town. It is 110 degrees in the shade, and Mamadou's blue denim shirt feels sticky and hot. He looks at the silent Vulture Tree through the green leaves of a baobab tree and then looks away, down the dirt street of M'Baykoro. The houses line the street in two long rows. The houses are round and white and made of mud. Their roofs are shaped like cones and are made of yellow thatch.

At the end of the street is the mosque, where Mamadou goes to study the Koran every week, and on a bench in front of the mosque sits an old man dressed in a fine linen bubu. He sits proudly and silently in the shade of the white mosque. His name is Seydou Kieta. Many years ago, before Mali was a free country, he made a pilgrimage to Mecca. The trip was hard because Seydou Kieta took the route to the north, which passes through Timbuktu and plunges into the Sahara Desert. Now he is too old to make another pilgrimage to the holy city of Islam.

Beside him sits a stranger in khaki shirt and pants, a calabash of cool water beside his feet. He drinks from a cup of water and passes the cup to the old man, who accepts it with a gentle nod of the head. The stranger is a black engineer from Bamako, the capital of Mali. For two weeks he and his helpers have been planning and mapping the new road which will pass by M'Baykoro.

Once, not too many years ago, nobody would have talked to a stranger. But now Mali is a free country. The French have left. Mali belongs to her people, and her people work together.

Last week, Mamadou spoke to the stranger. The stranger put his hand on Mamadou's shoulder and said:

2

"What are those books you are carrying?"

"I'm going to school," answered Mamadou.

"And then," asked the engineer, "what will you do for Mali?"

"I want to be an engineer. Like you. I want to build things. I want to build roads. I want to build factories," answered Mamadou, and the stranger nodded and said, "Good."

Today the engineer is talking to Seydou Kieta, who knows the Koran and the stories of Old Mali.

Mamadou leaves the shade of the baobab tree and walks to the mosque. "Will you tell us a story of Old Mali

And Muhammad was pleased by the wisdom of Bilali and made him the first muezzin of Islam. It was the voice of Bilali which called the faithful to prayer—his voice which made all believers turn toward Mecca and toward the temple Ka'bah, wherein is the Black Stone and the mystery of Allah.

But the descendants of Bilali left the land of the Arabs and they traveled south across the Sahara to settle here in our lands. They were black men and they settled in a black land.

Nare-Famakan was of the generations of Bilali and it is with him that my story begins, for Nare-Famakan was the first King of Mali and begot twelve sons, of whom the youngest was Sundiata.

* * * * *

One day the King and his hunters rested by the banks of a river called the Sankarani. All that morning and afternoon they had followed the track of an elephant whose stride was six paces long. And now, as the sun began to set, they paused to drink and talk of the hunt. They were simbon—master hunters—and they did not whisper like frightened women but spoke aloud and laughed, although the region was unknown to them.

The wind brushed the grasses around them. The water of the river was clear and good, and the land was rich. In the plains beyond their camp the hunters heard the sound of much game.

6

So Nare-Famakan drew apart from his men and sat alone by the river. He dug his hands into the good soil and let the earth spill out between his fingers. Then he stood up.

"Let this be our new home," he said very quietly. His hunters turned and looked at him. Their voices were stilled. Against the last rays of a setting sun, the King's face shone like polished ebony. He pointed to a great baobab tree standing alone at the foot of a hill.

"We will be like that tree," he said, "for the branches of the baobab reach back down to earth and take root so that one tree has many trunks. Like the baobab we will take root a thousand times in this new land."

His simbon stood and faced their King. They were not afraid of the darkness or the unknown land. They raised the hunter's cry of joy:

"Wassa wassa . . . ai-ye. Wassa wassa . . . ai-ye."

And at that place, by the river Sankarani, Nare-Famakan built his capital and called it Niani.

Nare-Famakan was a man of justice and peace, so

that men gathered at Niani from all the lands of the Niger River basin, which is our blood and our life. They came from the Bafing River tribes, which are in the wide land of the antelope, and from the Niagoucle Mountains, rich in gold, and even Arabs from the windswept desert sands came to sit by the side of Nare-Famakan.

And the King spread woven reed mats upon the ground and set gourds of icy water beside him, and all men came to share a place by his side and also a cool drink of water.

Indeed, Allah blessed the works of Nare-Famakan.

But no man may escape his destiny, for what is written is written. The wind will not sweep it away and the rains will not wash it into the sea.

The day came when destiny cast its shadow upon the land of Mali. A force as arid and unyielding as the mountains rose up against Nare-Famakan—and struck!

And that force was Sumanguru the Accursed.

Book 2

This is the man who was Sumanguru:

He was a warrior king, born of warrior kings. He was a man born to lead and command. When Sumanguru walked, he strode erect as a giraffe and he was taller than all men.

But his eyes burned with a fury and hatred which made even the simbon turn away in fear. And they say that the buffalo, fiercest of all the animals, fled across the brown grasslands and hid like old women when Sumanguru passed. And it was because of the eyes.

For his eyes were the eyes of a snake, which never blink but fix upon its prey and burn like fire. Eyes that never smile, eyes that hide forever what the mind is plotting. Look! look into the eyes of the snake and you will see nothing—no, not even in the eyes of the black mamba, whose bite turns muscle and sinew into stone—but know that what hides behind those eyes is death.

So it was with Sumanguru. No man dared to stand before him, and those pale Arabs who came to him from the regions of the Sahara seemed like tattered white flags come to beg truce of a black fortress.

His capital was at Sosso, and his people feared him.

* * * * *

"Ya-ya-ya."

The sun burned overhead.

"Ya-ya-ya."

The wild boar turned and stretched its gray neck into the wind.

"Ya-ya-ya."

Downwind came the smell of men. The angry beast lowered its massive head and its tusks were like knives.

In his hands Sumanguru balanced the iron-shafted spear and the weight felt good in his hands. Alone, he stood on the burning grassland and faced the wild boar, a thing which no man had done before.

Again, Sumanguru shouted, "Ya-ya-ya."

Silently the animal turned, and silently he charged. His tusks tore through the brown stubble of the grass.

Dust flew as hoofs pounded the dry earth. The sun burned overhead. The red pig-eye of the boar burned.

But Sumanguru waited, then struck. Once, twice, six times the iron shaft bit deeply as the beast charged and turned and charged again. And then the beast bellowed once and turned its belly to the sun.

The dust had not yet settled when the signal drums began to speak. Across the broad grasslands they spoke of the King of Tabon, who was traveling through the lands of Sumanguru.

Now Sumanguru signaled to one of his men. "Go tell the King of Tabon that I, Sumanguru, King of Sosso and slayer of the boar, await him here. And give him this." With his knife, Sumanguru cut the heart out of the boar and gave it to the messenger.

But when the messenger returned he was alone. He fell upon his knees before Sumanguru and lowered his eyes.

"Where is the King of Tabon?"

"Master, he will not come."

"Where is the King!"

The slave trembled. "He will not come. To my words he answered, 'What is Sumanguru? Is it an animal or a bird?' and his men laughed with him.

" 'Moreover, you will tell Sumanguru, whatever that thing may be, that the King of Tabon goes to Niani, where Nare-Famakan rules and teaches the law of Allah,' the King said as they rode off. Master, they will not come to Sosso, but flung your offering into the brush."

In his heart, Sumanguru knew anger. He could taste it in his mouth, bitter as the leaf of the cola-nut tree. He sent his servants away and stood alone.

"Sosso is too small. Sosso is nothing." Silent before the wild boar, Sumanguru dreamed of power—the power that destroys, the power that burns proud cities, that makes slaves of free men and kings, and makes women grovel in the dust and cry over the bodies of husbands, fathers, and all kinsmen.

Then Sumanguru cursed Nare-Famakan. He raised his clenched fist and cursed the name of Allah, and of Muhammad, Prophet of the Lord. And he wept bitter tears.

And as he wept, from the region of the sandstone mountains a bird appeared and settled upon the carcass of the wild boar. It was an owl, the bird of ill omen. Silently it looked upon Sumanguru and he was afraid.

He turned away. The proud words he had flung against the Lord of Muhammad clung to his mouth like a handful of bitter dust. The bird meant death.

But Sumanguru stopped. In the dust before him appeared a large, gray stone. As he watched, the stone began to squirm. It was alive. A twisted arm stretched up from the gray mass and two eyes, rimmed in red, opened and fixed upon the face of Sumanguru.

13

"Who are you," barked Sumanguru. "How dare you sit before me without paying your respect to me? How dare you block my path?"

Those were the words of a brave man. But in his heart Sumanguru was afraid and the dwarf opened his crooked mouth and laughed, but he did not move aside.

The slayer of the wild boar backed away and turned toward Sosso. Before him in the dust sat the dwarf. Sumanguru turned toward the south. The dwarf sat before him in the dust. Sumanguru turned toward the north. The dwarf sat before him in the dust of the land.

Now wherever Sumanguru turned, the dwarf appeared before him. Sumanguru turned no longer. He was like the eland when it is attacked by the wild dogs of the grasslands. Trapped, the eland ceases its flight and with lowered neck and glazed eye waits for death, nor does it struggle anymore.

And the dwarf saw that and laughed again and spoke. His voice rustled like dry leaves.

"The owl is mine. I am the master of the owls. I have heard the great simbon, slayer of the wild boar, speak and I have come."

"I did not call you."

"Nay, but you cursed my enemy, and that makes you my friend, Sumanguru."

"I cursed no man," lied Sumanguru.

"You cursed Allah."

14

Book 3

Now the dwarf smiled. "Come sit beside me here in the dust of the land, mighty simbon."

"I will stand." Sumanguru thrust his spear into the earth. His eye became firm and steady. "Speak, dwarf. Say what you will say."

And who will say that Sumanguru was then a coward? I am old, children of Mali, and I have stood beside brave men as they faced death. Aye, how beautiful they were, the sinews of their necks like twisted ropes of iron, their lower lips pulled down to bare their teeth. But two moments before death they called upon Allah. One moment before their death they were silent. And dying, they screamed "N'na"—mother—and died like babies. N'na!

Yet Sumanguru stood. He was a man.

The dry voice of the dwarf began again, nor could Sumanguru tell when the voice stopped and the rustling of the grasses began.

"Sumanguru Kante, your people were here in these lands before all others. They were iron workers skilled in the arts of sorcery, as are all iron workers. Hear me, Sumanguru: I was before Allah was, and this land has always known me. Your father knew me, and his father before him. It was I who taught your ancestors how to use fire and work iron; I who taught your people how to make the iron shaft which today killed that beast. Look! see how the flies attack him now, fearlessly. Come sit beside me here in the dust of the land, mighty simbon."

But Sumanguru stood, though his legs were like the tender grass of spring, which yields to every touch of the wind.

Then the dwarf spoke of death, the death of cities and men and crops and grain. "I have destroyed nations and yet you dare stand before me. Come sit beside me, here in the dust of the land, mighty simbon."

Still Sumanguru stood. And seeing that his words of ancestors and words of death would not move Su-

manguru, the dwarf spoke out the thoughts of Sumanguru:

"Men fear me, but the sun does not. Like the meanest
hippopotamus that roils in the muddy waters of the Bani
River, fearful lest the burning sun should blister its fat
skin, I am forced to hide under thatched roofs with
women and children against the white fire of the afternoon sun."

At those words, Sumanguru shivered. The dwarf continued:

"And my subjects give me gold, but in the dry season
the sky does not send me a single drop of water for my
parched fields, and my cattle die, becoming carrion for
the vulture and the hyena."

Sumanguru shivered again.

"And children imitate my far-flung stride, but the
wind makes me stagger and shorten my steps," droned
the dwarf. "I am weak. I am nothing. The sun is stronger
than I am, and the rain more important, and the wind
more stubborn."

Unbidden, Sumanguru now sat, his legs of grass sur-
rendering. "Who told you these things? Who told you
my thoughts?"

But the dwarf did not answer. He bent his head low
and ran his left hand across the ground, smoothing it.
Then he dropped a handful of sand on the ground and

18

drew his fingers slowly across the sand. "Shall I read the sands, Sumanguru?"

"Read," whispered Sumanguru as he leaned forward to observe the soothsayer's art.

The dwarf began the reading. "I see twelve kings." He erased the lines upon the sand and began again. "Twelve kings and eleven kings dead. I see the skins of eleven dead kings stretched out like mats within the royal chamber of some great king. A sorcerer king sits upon the flayed skins of defeated kings."

"What king?" asked Sumanguru.

"And now I see . . . I see a fortress seven stories high. A tower seven stories high within a city which has three walls around it."

"The city. Tell me the city."

"I see . . . Look, look at the sands, Sumanguru. Look because they tell everything."

"I cannot read the sands, dwarf. What is the city; who is the sorcerer king?"

"And on the seventh story of the tower is the royal chamber and I see a box and in that box are fetishes of great power. O what a king. He rules over everything. Niani falls down before his army. Ghana falls down before his army. All fall down before his army."

"Curse you, dwarf. I command it: who is that sorcerer king?"

Now the dwarf sat back. "All fall down before him, Sumanguru."

Sumanguru raged. *"Who is he?"*

"All fall down before him, Sumanguru. Down before the sorcerer king. Down, down before him they fall, Sumanguru."

"Is it me? Curse you, deformed beast that you are. *Is it me?"*

Now the dwarf arose from the ground. Standing, he was smaller than Sumanguru who still squatted in the dust. "The man who dares follow me to the sandstone mountains, now, is that king."

And Sumanguru followed the owl and the dwarf, and went south into the sandstone mountains, where nothing lives. And there he made a pact with the djinns and afreets, unholy demons of the earth and sky, and they marked him as one of theirs. From the soles of his feet to the crown of his head, Sumanguru was covered by large, ash-white splotches. Sumanguru returned to Sosso —ugly. And he spoke to no man.

But now Sosso grew. Workers came, although no one knew from where they came. They spoke, but no one understood their language. Three walls they built around Sosso, each wall taller than the last. And in the center of Sosso a tower was built, seven stories high.

Book 4

According to the proverb: The monkey jabbers all through life and is silent only after death, but beware of the lion when it is silent.

Sumanguru the Accursed now moved like a lion and prepared warriors and weapons in the silence of the night, while Niani opened her gates to all men and slumbered in the darker silence of fate.

Within the gates of Niani, Arab traders met around the evening fires, and Ghanaians from the land of gold. They spoke of the Franks, who lived beyond the seas and rode into battle in cloth of iron, with iron shoes and iron gloves, atop horses draped in iron. Savage men, the Arabs

divination as all smiths are, was short but his shoulders
were like those of a bull. His arms had broken men. His
hands had snapped iron. Farakurun came to his King
and looked upon the stranger.

From his leather pouch, the stranger now pulled out
the twelve cowrie shells of the soothsayer's art and threw
them upon the ground.

"See how he casts the shells and how they fall. Mark
this man's words, my King," said Farakurun.

"At these gates, on the last day of the full moon, will
appear a woman," intoned the stranger. "Look upon
her, Nare-Famakan, and bid her sit within your house,
for she is ugly and men will laugh at her ugliness. Yet

she will bring a soun—thief—who will be more noble than Alexander the Great. And he will be called the King with Two Names."

Having said this, the stranger soon departed from Niani, his task accomplished.

Now Nare-Famakan was greatly puzzled by these remarks. Alexander the Great was the conqueror of whom the Arabs spoke, whose fame had spread even to the flood plains of the Niger River and among the hunters of the Adamoua Mountains. But what thief could be a conqueror, and who was the ugly woman?

All that month, Nare-Famakan asked these questions of the Council of Elders. But they shook their heads and were silent. So he stood alone and puzzled, on the appointed night, and observed a solitary figure marching like a man across the grasslands bathed in moonlight. The figure approached the gates and still Nare-Famakan waited. Then, by the light of torchbearers, he saw that it was a woman, a woman with a flat, ugly face and bulging eyes the size of vulture's eggs.

"Surely that is the woman foretold by the stranger," said Nare-Famakan, smiling, "for I have never seen uglier." And Kekotonki laughed.

"Even so," muttered Farakurun, "it is as the stranger said: men will laugh at her ugliness."

At this, Nare-Famakan grew thoughtful. "What is

25

your name, woman?" he asked. "What is your tribe and who are your people and why do you come alone across the grasslands, marching like a man so fearlessly?"

"I am Sogolon Koudouma and I have come," was all she answered. And to all other questions, "I am Sogolon Koudouma and I have come," was her only answer.

That night, Nare-Famakan sacrificed an ox to the spirits of the land and to the ancestors. That night, seeing that the sacrifice was good, Nare-Famakan took Sogolon Koudouma to wife, and that night she conceived.

* * * * *

When the season of the rains returned and the streets of Niani were rivers of mud, flowing like the Sankarani River, Nare-Famakan was called to the side of his child-bearing wife. Slowly, the King returned to his palace from the mosque, leaning on the arm of Farakurun. He walked into the main chamber and saw the fine buffalo hides and the strong, soaring peak of the thatched roof above his head, and he was pleased. Then he walked out into the walled compound wherein were the houses of his wives.

But within the house of Sogolon there was silence. No voices rejoiced in the birth of a son and Sogolon wept silently. Midwives drew back from the King as he entered, and cast their eyes to the earth.

26

A son had been born and he was named Mari Diata. But he was ugly, uglier than his mother.

Seeing that, Nare-Famakan shook his head sadly. Mari Diata would be no Alexander the Great to conquer far-flung lands. His legs though straight seemed weak. His enormous head flopped from side to side like a stone upon a string.

"He is as formless as mud. He is rooted to the earth," thought Farakurun.

Nare-Famakan was now an old man. His skin no longer glistened but hung like cloth from his bones. More-over, runners from surrounding tribes had come to Niani to speak of some great, unholy danger: a sorcerer king, half gray, half black, who could transform himself into sixty-nine different beasts, and who led an army of con-querors, was destroying the land.

Knowing that he was old and that Niani was in danger, Nare-Famakan saw the boy and was uneasy.

Farakurun said: "Mari Diata will be King of Niani. He will be like Alexander the Great."

Kekotonki said: "You have eleven sons. You cannot leave Niani in the hands of a baby."

The other wives of Nare-Famakan spoke: "Alexander the Great was the King of Gold and Silver. This baby shall be called the King of Frogs and Toads. Choose a king from among our sons instead."

27

Nare-Famakan turned to the people of Niani, for a king is no king who does not listen to his subjects. And after great debate, Nare-Famakan selected Kononioko Simba, his eldest son, and passed to him the scepter of authority.

Then Nare-Famakan died. May Allah preserve him.

Book 5

One hot night in the dry season while lions coughed, Sumanguru sat in his chamber at the top of the tower of Sosso. In the center of the round room an earthen tub filled with greenish water swirled endlessly, until the snake which dwelled within it lifted his head. The lidless eyes fixed upon Sumanguru.

"Master. Master. Call them tonight," whispered the snake, and then slipped back into the brackish water of the tub.

"Master" he was called, but Sumanguru the Accursed was the slave of those nameless powers who had marked him. Slowly he turned toward the wooden case where he stored his fetishes. The lid opened at his approach and he reached within the box, removing strange herbs and roots which he flung into the brazier.

A bluish fire burned, then glowed dully. Sumanguru cried, "Now!" in the smoke-filled chamber.

And they came, calling him master. Some were without shape, and some without substance. They hovered in the air and settled into dark corners, waiting.

"He told me to call you," said Sumanguru.

At those words one of the afreets slipped into the center of the room and pulled the twelve cowrie shells of the soothsayer's art out of a leather pouch. With his left hand, the hand of evil, he cast the shells upon the wooden floor and examined them.

"Fear one of twelve, Master," he said at last.

Sumanguru frowned. "What does that mean," he muttered. The afreet cast the shells again. "To the east was a man, King of Niani——"

"Nare-Famakan," hissed Sumanguru.

"Beware of his sons. I read the shells and they say that one of twelve will be king over all these lands, defeating you in battle."

Now Sumanguru laughed. "Are you not behind me and is not my magic more powerful than even the word of Allah? Why should I fear the sons of Nare-Famakan? The world trembles at my very name. The people hide in fear and obey me because of the power which crushes everything."

The afreet answered nothing, but cast the brittle shells a third time. "When the mountain moves against you, Sosso shall fall in ruins. That is what the shells tell me, Master."

"That will never be. Yet, Niani's time has come. I shall destroy it," answered the Sorcerer King.

* * * * *

The drums of Sosso sounded and the army assembled. Its spears were as many as the grasses of the plains, and no man could count them all. Upon his black stallion, Sumanguru led his army across the grasslands and down toward the Niger River. There he paused to prepare his battalions for the attack.

And now a runner appeared before Kononioko Simba, King of Niani.

"Great King, I bear witness to a strange event. I am a herder from the village of Kasolla. Two nights ago, as I stood with my brother on the bank of the Niger, a strange sound came to us. A sound, O mighty King, like the drone of winged insects. I looked across the river into the gathering night. The lowering sun still touched the tops of the Niagouele Mountains, yet the mountains were black."

Now the elders of Niani heard this and were afraid. "The water spirits are angry at us. We have done them an injustice and this is a sign of their anger."

"Let the water spirits take care of the unknown, and man take care of what may be known, Little Father," said the King. Then, "Bougari," he commanded, pointing to Niani's bravest warrior, "you will take fifteen armed men. Return with this herder across the flat land where the elephant herd was seen four days ago. See what this man has seen and return to us."

"Do not risk the anger of the spirits," broke in the spokesman of the elders. "When the thunder roars, what man may shout louder?" He meant: men cannot struggle against things greater than themselves.

"Aye," answered Kononioko Simba, "but when the fisherman has paid due honor to the gods and carries the fishing amulet about his neck, which is pleasing to the gods, then he takes his spear and his fishing nets and works all day, sweating in the sun." He meant: the gods can only do so much. Afterward, man must act.

Thus men argued in council, speaking in the old parables of our people. For wise men speak in parables and do honor to the wisdom of the past.

Finally, Kononioko Simba prevailed and Bougari set off across the grasslands. Fourteen summers Bougari had lived. He was a man and unafraid. When he returned he came before his King. "Yes," he said, "the foothills of the Niagouele Mountains are black, even in the daylight. The huts of the herders are burning and the herders, food for all vultures, are scattered around the smoking embers.

33

The army of Sosso is on the march. As far as I could see, the mountains were black—with warriors!"

* * * * *

"I fear this day," muttered Kononioko Simba. He stood before his lines and held the three-edged sword of his father across his shoulder. Behind Kononioko Simba waited the warriors of Niani. Before him in the distance, droning like insects, advanced the army of Sumanguru. The sun was burning. There was no wind.

"Bougari," ordered the King, "take your archers along the eastern ridge. Hide there. I will draw Sumanguru's army through the gully between the hills. I will pretend to retreat in fear. Then, as his army follows us, you will open fire. As the buffalo fights by slashing with his horns, first to the left, then to the right, so your archers will be like the hook of the right horn. When Sumanguru turns to attack you upon the ridge, I will counterattack his exposed flank. That will be the hook of the left horn."

So the King laid his plans and deployed his cavalry as Sumanguru's army rushed down upon him.

The dust raised by the sorcerer's army stretched from horizon to horizon. Beasts of the plains—lion, antelope, and eland—fled before that army as animals flee before the bush-beaters seeking to stampede game into traps. The army of Niani stood motionless, waiting, while the crazed animals rushed through the line of warriors as if they were harmless trees. Lion and antelope ran side by side, brothers in fear.

Now the army of Sosso flooded into the gully. The drums began the signal of the Attack Which Never Ends. The spears lowered like the horn of the attacking rhinoceros. The droning insect-sound became the roar of the rain-swollen river.

Yet, until the final moment came, Kononioko Simba stood and the three-edged sword did not tremble upon his shoulder. "Now!" cried that doomed King, and his army pretended to break and run. Horses screamed. Men flung their spears away and turned and ran.

The army of Sumanguru sent up a cry of triumph.

And then Bougari's archers spoke. The sun was blotted out by the black rush of arrows, whispering, singing, screaming through the air like a host of bees. Day became night under that terrible cloud.

Around Sumanguru, men began to fall. The attack wavered. Sumanguru turned toward the ridge. "Wind," he ordered. "The wind." And a wind came out of hell and burst along the ridge. Archers tumbled like twigs.

"My wind, my wind. Give me my wind," howled Sumanguru. "Give me my wind." And the wind redoubled in its fury. The ridge vanished in dust and shrieking storm.

"The wind. The wind." Sumanguru stretched his hands to the pale sky. "The wind," he screamed. And

then he laughed, for in the gully there was no wind nor breath of air. But along the ridge ran the killing wind of hell.

"Forward, cowards," yelled Sumanguru, his voice swollen with rage and joy. He flung the weight of his forces against Kononioko Simba, King of Niani.

* * * * *

Across the field of battle women moved liked shadows, wailing, gathering the bodies of their men into their arms.

Seeing that, Sumanguru spoke to himself as he walked among the dead and dying warriors of Niani.

"Listen. Men die as they are born: in the arms of women. Listen to the weeping. Sumanguru has made this city weep."

From the gates of Niani flowed the men of Sosso, carrying booty on their heads. And that night, on the floor of the seventh story of the tower of Sosso, the skin of Kononioko Simba lay stretched out like a reed mat. And Sumanguru walked upon it.

* * * * *

O children of Mali, what more shall I say? The seasons came and went, and one by one the sons of Nare-Famakan ascended to the throne of a dying city. Nine good men and warriors, one after another, took up the scepter of authority. They were: Kabali Simba, Mare Taniakale, Nutuye Mare Yeressegue, Sossoturu Lakandia, Mossokoro, Mosse Kandake, Mansa Makamba, Finadugu Komakam, and Gaga Bougari, the brave warrior. Each in turn stood up against the army of Sosso, and each in turn was defeated and his skin stretched out upon the floor of the tower of Sosso. And each in turn felt the weight of Sumanguru's foot.

Only two sons of Nare-Famakan survived: Kalabamba Diokunto and Mari Diata.

But to the people of Niani, dying under the yoke of Sumanguru, there was only one son left. For Mari Diata was a cripple and a thief.

Book 6

"Out. Out. Get out."

Some thing rolled out of a hut and crawled across the dust like a snake.

"The son of Sogolon is stealing again," muttered Kekotonki to Farakurun.

"Accursed beast! Why cannot he walk? Look, look at him crawling on his belly," answered Farakurun bitterly.

Aye, Mari Diata crawled. He was rooted to the earth, dust-covered and fat. His useless legs dragged behind him and dug furrows into the earth. He could not stand like a man.

Sogolon rushed out of her hut. "Leave my Mari Diata

alone," she screamed at the woman who had chased her son out into the road, beating him with a bundle of firewood. "Leave the future King alone."

The woman stopped her beating and laughed in the cruel way of mockery so special to women, a laughter which pierced Sogolon to the heart. "Future King? This grub, this thief who cannot walk? Do not all the women of Niani shut their doors against your worthless son because he steals? They say the lion is the greatest thief of Africa, yet I know a greater one. Mari Diata is his name, but better he were called Soun Diata—Thief-Lion—your crippled Soun Diata."

At this last remark many who stood in the street laughed and one called out, "Run, Sundiata, or the lion hunter will beat you with her bundle of sticks."

Then Farakurun said, "Do you remember the words of the stranger who came, many years ago, bringing word of a conqueror as great as Alexander? It was he who foretold the coming of Sogolon."

"I remember," answered Kekotonki.

"And remember that he said: A great soun, a thief with two names, will come. I tell you, Kekotonki, that this was foretold. Did I not see how the stranger cast the cowrie shells? This crawling child is the thief who will free Niani. He is the King with Two Names: Mari Diata and Sundiata."

"O Farakurun, forget the past and look upon Niani."

Kekotonki swept his hand from side to side. "Our houses are rotting. Look, see how the roofs sag and the earthen walls crumble. See how our children walk with swollen bellies, dying of hunger. And our cattle are taken by Sumanguru. He comes and goes out of Niani at his pleasure, taking our fairest children as slaves. You have become old, Farakurun. Nay, no cripple will save our dying city. We are stricken by a plague called Sumanguru the Accursed. Not even traders from beyond the desert come to us anymore. And see, look there at the eleventh son of Nare-Famakan. Kalabamba Diokunto cringes before Sumanguru and calls him 'Master.' Kalabamba Diokunto lives among the women and will not hunt nor lead his people but giggles within the compound walls and drinks palm wine brought from Nigeria. Our last King is no more than a woman."

Just then a lookout on the crumbling wall called out: "He comes. The Master comes. Sound the drums of honor."

Followed by his men, Sumanguru was coming across the grasslands for his monthly share of the harvest and many cattle besides.

"Did you say, 'He comes'?" cried Kalabamba Diokunto from within his hut. Soon he was rushing along the streets crying, "Bring out your fairest children so that the Master may choose."

Farakurun clenched his gnarled hands and looked

down at the ground beneath his feet. "You are no King, but an insect," he muttered darkly. The words of the weak King brought tears to his eyes, for there are worse things than death.

Sumanguru marched into town to the sound of drums. The people trembled and Sumanguru smiled.

"You are early this month. The harvest is not yet in, Master," stammered Kalabamba Diokunto as he looked down at Sumanguru's feet. He did not dare look higher than that, from fear of the terrible eyes.

Suddenly, Sumanguru placed his heavy hands upon Kalabamba's shoulders and smiled. "Dear Kalabamba, why call me 'Master'? Call me brother instead. Say it. Say 'Brother' to me and I will call you brother also."

"Bro—Brother . . ." stammered the King.

"Louder, louder, Brother. Let all Niani hear that we are brothers, that it may rejoice at your good fortune."

"Brother!" said Kalabamba Diokunto. "Brother." And now the foolish King began to strut about like a rooster displaying his feathers. "You, Kekotonki." He pointed at that unhappy man. "I have heard you whispering behind my back, saying evil things. We shall settle this when my brother is gone."

"Good, Brother. Make them cringe in terror, for that is the only joy there is," shouted Sumanguru.

"And you also, Farakurun, for you are a useless old

man!" Now Kalabamba Diokunto wagged his head from side to side and laughed.

But Sumanguru wearied of his game. "Kill him," he said and Kalabamba Diokunto fell under the knives.

"Where," Sumanguru now asked, "is the twelfth and last son of Nare-Famakan, that unfortunate ruler?"

Kekotonki pointed mutely to Sundiata, named Mari Diata, who still lay in the dust beside his mother's feet.

Sumanguru strode up to him and looked down. "How old are you, future King of all Niani?" he demanded.

"He is seven," replied Kekotonki.

"Let him speak for himself!" snarled the King of Sosso, "I have just made him a king."

"He has never spoken."

"Then let him stand before me."

"He cannot stand."

So Sumanguru crouched beside the boy. "I have come to pay my respects, O King of Niani. I grieve the loss of your fine brothers and their deaths sadden me."

Sundiata looked into the terrible eyes of Sumanguru. "I will walk now," said the boy, and they were the first words he had ever spoken. He struggled to rise but his knees would not hold him up and he slipped back into the dust.

"A stick, get him a stick," ordered Farakurun. A stunned villager gave his walking stick to the outstretched

45

hands of the boy. Again, Sundiata struggled to rise, leaning on the stick, but the stick broke under his weight.

"You," shouted Farakurun to one of his assistants, "get me a bar of iron. Quickly."

The bar of iron was brought. The boy took it in his arms and propped it in the ground. Again he struggled to rise but the bar twisted and bent in half, and still Sundiata did not rise.

"In my shop you will find a rod of iron which three men cannot lift with ease. Go fetch it," ordered the smith. Soon, struggling men returned with the heavy bar and rolled it to the foot of the boy. Effortlessly, Sundiata propped it up and struggled to rise. And the rod twisted and bent in half, and still Sundiata did not rise.

"What sorcery is this?" muttered Sumanguru to himself. Everybody was silent. Nobody dared to move. Sweat poured out of Sundiata in a flood, and still he lay in the dust, his useless legs stretched out before him.

"I know," shouted Kekotonki. "Bring him the scepter of the kings."

The thin reed, symbol of Niani's power, was brought to the child. The scepter weighed no more than a hollow gourd, yet Sundiata grasped it in his hands and rose from his prison of earth.

Now, on shaking limbs, Sundiata smiled up at Sumanguru the Accursed and said: "I am glad you grieve the loss of my brothers, who were dear to me also. Yet more will you sorrow in time to come."

Sumanguru backed away, then laughed. "We will meet again later, my little thief. For a large mat is worth more to me than a small one. And there are other regions for me to conquer."

Sumanguru left the city of Niani and returned to his castle, shaken.

Book 7

As Sumanguru departed across the grasslands, Sundiata's mother sang:

Bhi O bhi, bika dhi lhe he
Mansa Allah ma bhinyo kondan

("Today, this is a great today for me.
My Lord Allah never gave me better.")

At those words the people emerged from behind their walls and gathered in the street to look at Sundiata.

"Does he walk?" "Look, look at him——" "I heard

him speak——" "Sumanguru fled——" "Sundiata walks, he walks——" babbled the villagers. "What does this mean, Farakurun?" the people demanded.

"Let us meet at the baobab tree where once Nare-Famakan sat, teaching the word of Allah and dispensing justice," said Kekotonki. He did not lead the people to the tree but stayed behind and kicked, kicked savagely at the brown stain upon the earth where Kalabamba Diokunto had bled to death. Then, when the forgetful earth had covered that last shame of a proud people, Kekotonki walked slowly to the tree.

Seven years of defeat had made of him a silent, ragged man. Yet hope never dies, but burns brightly when it is almost dead, as the last embers flare up suddenly to reveal faces around the campfire.

As Kekotonki approached, Bala Fasseke of the silver words was speaking. He told of the stranger and the words of the stranger and of the sorrow of Niani.

And now Farakurun spoke, saying, "Bala Fasseke, you have spoken well. Every great king has had a griot—storyteller—to spread his fame, to explain his deeds, and to teach him the wisdom of our ancestors, without which no man may rule justly or wisely. Become the griot of Sundiata and teach him well."

And then, to celebrate the moment, Bala Fasseke composed a song to the young King:

Na da dinyo di ia
Sundiata na da dinge di ia
Na da dinyo di ia
Mari Diata na da dinyo di ia

("You have come bringing joy to the world.
Sundiata has come to make the world happy.
You have come bringing joy to the world.
Mari Diata has come to make the world happy.")

Then the King's bafalon was brought out and Bala Fasseke gently struck the wooden keys and the listeners fell silent, for music is beyond words and tells of gods and of life. Like liquid gold, like fire, like an endless river, the notes sprang into life. Some men cried, for only the weak dare not cry, and as the music soared up and across the sunswept grasslands, the people danced and sang:

Ton ta Diata
Ton ta Manding
Ton ta Di-a-ta
Ton ta Mannnnnnnnn-ding

("Take up the armor, lion;
Take up Mali's armor.")

The Lion of Niani was awake. Sundiata had risen from the earth. For nine months he had grown in the belly of his mother. For seven years he had grown in the belly of the earth. And now he was born.

Aye, sing, children of Mali. Sing, Bala Fasseke. Your songs have come down to us. Sing, sing because song is our blood and our brotherhood. We shall always sing your words. We have not forgotten them.

After the song, Sundiata took the man-breaking hand of Farakurun in his and walked away from the baobab tree, and the people fell back silently.

"The people fall back from me, Old Father," said the little Lion, still caked with the dust of seven years of crawling.

"Know that the hero is a lonely stranger, Sundiata. And know also that once men hated you for a thief and a cripple, for men hate the weak, and now they will hate you because you stride like the gods, for men hate the strong."

Thus Sundiata walked and began to learn wisdom. Before the season of the rains began, Sundiata had stalked and killed his first elephant.

Before the first rains began, his enemies plotted against him.

* * * * *

Her name was Sassouma Berete, and she had been the

wife of Nare-Famakan until he took Sogolon as wife. For seven years she had rejoiced at the crippled boy and laughed when his mother passed, saying, "My sons walked at the beginning. Dear Sister, let one of my sons go to harvest your grain since your son is so useless." And for seven years Sogolon wept bitter tears while Sassouma Berete laughed.

But now Sundiata walked and Sassouma sought out the Niagouan Mossu—the Nine Witches—and spoke:

"The thief walks. People honor his passing and his coming. But mark what I say, ancient hags: he will follow the God of the Arabs as his father did. He will pick up the sword of Allah and drive you from your land and set your house to the torch."

In the darkness of the hut the hags answered in whispered unison: "The father did not chase. The son will not chase."

"But this one will. I have heard him say this, for I love him dearly and he confides in me, knowing my love for him." This and other lies said Sassouma Berete. And every day she appeared at the hut of the Niagouan Mossu, bringing them crushed grain and fine cloth. And every day she lied, until the hags were fearful and shut their door against all people except Sassouma Berete.

"But no charm can work, no curse can work, work against one who has done us no injury," they said in whispered unison.

"Then go to his mother's vegetable garden. Pretend to steal the crop. When he sees that, the fatherless boy will curse you and drive you away. Then will your spells work."

And this the Niagouan Mossu did.

"See, he comes. Now, sisters, now pick and dig the roots and trample the grain and pull it out, pull it out," they whispered, bending and picking, trampling the grain and pulling it out.

But Sundiata approached them and said, "Here, Old Mothers, I will help you. This garden is for all those who are hungry and we must learn to share what we have."

"You will not curse us?"

"Nay, but I will help you."

"But when you are grown, you will chase us, chase us from this land because we do not worship Allah."

"Why should I banish the earth from my lands? What would I stand upon? What would feed the people of Niani? Each thing has its due portion, and there is wisdom in the Niagouan Mossu as there is wisdom in the sky, which is the realm of Allah. Thus you are welcome to my crops and you are welcome in this land," answered the boy.

So the hags formed a circle around the boy and said:

"The lion hunts. The lion cub is fed and hides. Learn from us. Learn the wisdom of the earth, little Lion.

You have enemies here. Leave Niani. Leave, leave until
you are a lion. Leave a cub, come back a lion."

"I cannot leave."

"Leave. Learn from us. Did not Muhammad, Prophet
of your Lord Allah, flee to Yathrib from Mecca when
his enemies sought him out?"

This they said and other things, besides, so that Sundiata returned to his house and called for Farakurun and
Kekotonki.

"The Niagouan Mossu have spoken wisely," said
Kekotonki. "Sundiata has enemies everywhere. Sumanguru daily sends his spies to listen to the people. Soon
he will return and kill the boy."

"True," agreed Farakurun. "Moreover, our finest warriors are dead and guard the city with sightless eyes. Take your boy far from here, Sogolon. Go to our allies in the city of Tabon, which is well defended and strong. And you, Sundiata, remember that you are a king. Act like one."

"How does a king act?" asked the boy.

"The king knows his destiny. Allah has arranged all things so that they might obey His desires. What begins tomorrow was arranged before time itself began. Therefore surrender yourself to the will of Allah, the Merciful, the Beneficent, and all things shall come to pass as they were foretold. Remember the teaching of the Koran: that Muhammad, Prophet of the Lord, could not read. Yet the Angel Gabriel came unto him, saying, 'Read,' and Muhammad read. So Allah will come unto you, saying, 'Lead,' and you shall lead."

"But for now you must be gone before dawn," said Kekotonki. "I will arrange for horses. As exiles you will be a burden to friends, thus you will leave with only your mother and your sister, Meniemba Souko."

Sundiata left the side of Farakurun and walked out into the dark light. He was still a boy, not yet a man. Silently he stood by the iron gates of Niani. Farakurun had worked those gates into the shapes of animals and birds, knowing that the tree, the lion, and the things of

56

the earth were holy things. This is what Africa has always known and what Sundiata would come to know. But men like Sumanguru never learn the truth.

Now, as Sundiata stood by the iron gates, Doua, the man who spoke with drums, began to send a message on the long, four-legged signal drum. The sound rose and fell, imitating the rising and the falling of the human voice, for that is how the signal drum speaks.

After the message was sent, silence returned once again and Sundiata heard the trumpeting of elephants far over the warm grasslands. Then the signal drums beyond Kangare, to the north, repeated the message. Again a pause, the trumpeting of elephants, and the drums of Sido began to speak. The sound was so faint and distant that Sundiata had to hold his breath to listen as the message was driven deeper into the grasslands.

"My land," said Sundiata. Then he turned and crossed the silent streets. Within the round houses he heard laughter and the voices of men, and once he heard a child crying.

"My people."

Having said that, Sundiata was no longer a boy but not yet a king.

Book 8

In the morning, before sunrise, three horses rode quietly out of Niani. Niani was asleep. Niani would sleep for many years to come.

In this way the exiles fled Niani:

First crossing to the west bank of the Sankarani River, they rode to the Niger River below Siguiri. On the other shore of that river, south of the foothills of the Niagouele Mountains, begins the vast range of the Fouta Djalon. There is a valley there, ringed by mountains, where the Tinkisso River flows. Some men call the valley the Valley of the Spear Fishermen. The exiles rode six days through the valley until they reached its westernmost point. There, in the jaws of the mountains, the fortress town of Tabon stood as if reaching for the pale sky. Tabon, city of the region of waterfalls and rapids, soaring peaks and valleys. Tabon, hereditary friend of Niani.

Now, as the travelers climbed the ranging hills, the warriors of Tabon approached to escort them. Weapons flashed, iron weapons. Horses neighed. The drums sounded. In this way the King of Tabon, called the Fat King, greeted the advancing strangers and opened the gates of his city.

"If you have come in peace, dwell here in peace with us," said the King. Beside him stood Kemoko, sorcerer of Tabon.

"I am Sogolon, widow of Nare-Famakan. This is my son, Sundiata, and this is my daughter, Meniemba Souko. We are weary and need rest within your fortress, O mighty King of Tabon."

So the King greeted them as kinsmen and bade them enter, saying of Sundiata, "This one will be a king." He said many things which pleased the aging Sogolon, yet Sundiata was uneasy.

Through a maze of winding corridors the Fat King led his guests and spoke too much, ever turning his head and flashing eyes which were swollen with disease, and red. Now he led them into the throne room and sat upon his royal throne. It was carved from rare woods and inlaid with silver and ivory and the joints were made of bright copper. And the King of Tabon told the history of the throne and how its copper joints had come from the land of the Cisse, who were the descendants of Alexander the Great.

Then Sogolon began her tale of the flight from Niani and she repeated the words of Farakurun: "who was your friend of old, King of Tabon, when he hunted with you and shared the sweet flesh of the antelope."

But although the Fat King nodded and sadly shook his head and sighed when Sogolon sighed, his blood-red eyes were fixed upon Sundiata and slowly narrowed into tiny slits, so that soon neither red nor white could be seen, but only the black, glittering pupils.

Afterward, the King called for the servants and called for music and food.

"Indeed, I grieve with you for your misfortunes, little King, and I would welcome you as a brother, from love of your dead father and Farakurun also, who hunted the antelope with me. But my city is too humble to offer you comfort. Moreover, the region has a hard climate for those whose homes are in the grasslands. You are young and I am old, but were I your age I would go north, toward the desert regions and the land of the Valley of the Serpent. There might you live in a style as befits one who will soon rule."

Now Sundiata spoke up fearlessly: "You fear Sumanguru, who has killed my brothers and will kill your sons, O Fat King."

"Get out!" roared the enraged King of Tabon, shaking his fist at Sundiata. "Rest your horses and your bones this night but begone tomorrow, else I send you as a gift to Sumanguru as I would send fine, quartered meat."

Yet, as the exiles rode away down the slopes of the Fouta Djalon, the Fat King stood upon the ramparts of his fortress and was lost in thought. "He shall be a king, a great king, that little thief. I fear such boys as that one, Kemoko," he said to the sorcerer.

"One word from you——"

"No, let them be. Let them go in peace. Had he spoken those words with the voice of a man rather than the squeak of a boy, I would have trembled before him. Let them go in peace, so long as they go."

The baby takes a step and is called a child. The child takes a step and is called a man. What is the name of the next step, which few men dare to take? Tell me, children of Mali, the name of the step of the fearless Sundiata.

Book 9

The Bafing River reaches west into the land of the leopard, by the rapids of Ditinn in the Fouta Djalon, and north to the Senegal River.

The exiles followed the course of the Bafing River northward and then turned east toward Wagadu, crossing the Valley of the Serpent, where they heard the tale of the Serpent God.

Beyond the Valley of the Serpent began the land of the Arabs. Now, truly, Sundiata was an exile in an unknown region. Gone were the round houses with peaked roofs which shed water, for the Arabs live in terraced houses with flat roofs, among narrow streets, in a dry land by the edge of the sands of the Sahara.

In the streets, black Songhoi tribesmen tended round bread ovens taller than a man. In the brushland, which is the home of the Bella tribesmen, Sundiata saw the thatched huts of those people and heard their strange language.

Fierce Arabs of the desert rode by, dressed so that only their eyes showed, black and glittering. Yet they greeted the exiles as fellow Muslims and shared their water, their grain, and their meat freely.

In the city of Wagadu, Sundiata walked among the barbers who sat cross-legged in the streets and carefully shaved the heads and beards of men, dipping steel razors into bowls of water, while market women rushed by, balancing baskets on their heads.

Someday all of that would be the land of the people of Mali, but for Sundiata it was a land of exile.

Yet Sundiata was not friendless, for the princes of the region had sat by the side of Nare-Famakan. "You have come in peace, therefore live in peace among us," they said.

And the years passed and Sundiata grew and was no longer ugly. His voice was firm and the servants of his hosts obeyed his slightest command, for servants love to be commanded by leaders.

The princes of the land saw that Sundiata commanded

respect. They were pleased by this and spoke to him:

"We desire that you should go east across the edges of the desert to Mema, which is by the Niger River and is the city of our kinsmen. King Mussa Tunkara is a fierce warrior who loves strength and will teach you the arts of warfare. Moreover he is without children and you will please him."

So Sundiata set out across the sands and saw the things he had never seen: the storms of sand, the whirlwind, and the oasis where the sweet date grows.

At his approach to the city of Mema, Mussa Tunkara sent out his cavalry to greet the arriving prince and Sundiata wondered at the fine horses and armor of the warriors.

✳ ✳ ✳ ✳ ✳

For three long years Mussa Tunkara called Sundiata son and taught him the arts of warfare. After that, Sundiata led the cavalry of Mema and struck terror into the hearts of the hill men and won great battles.

For this reason, Mussa Tunkara called Sundiata before him: "Sundiata, my Son, I have taught you all I know about warfare. You are now a man of seventeen years and I wish to pass on to you the wisdom I have learned with age."

So the King began the story of Abu Kassim:

"In the city of Damascus there dwelt a man by the

name of Abu Kassim. He was a good trader but a bad man and the people of Damascus passed by his door and shunned him in the marketplace.

"When Abu Kassim died he went before the Lord Allah and saw the scribes who sit by His side and measure a man's good deeds against his bad.

"And beyond the Lord Allah was a great chasm, and at the bottom of that pit burned the fires of hell. On the other side was the land of the blessed, and for each man there was a bridge to cross.

"With every good deed, the bridge widened. With every bad deed, the bridge narrowed. Seeing that, Abu Kassim regretted everything. His bridge would be as narrow as the edge of a sword.

"By the side of the fiery pit, Abu Kassim saw a man who rolled his eyes in terror and shook like a leaf, for the bridge he had to cross was no wider than the palm of my hand.

"So Abu Kassim was moved to pity for the man and went to him. 'Take my good deeds as a gift, and may they widen your path,' he said. Thereupon, the bridge widened so that it was the width of two palms, and the man crossed to the other side.

"Now there was no bridge for Abu Kassim to cross, when suddenly a terrible voice thundered above him and said, 'That same bridge is also yours, Abu Kassim. Cross to the other side.'

and thus can be destroyed. Sumanguru has a taboo. Discover that taboo and use it against him, for it will destroy his powers of sorcery."

"And what is the taboo?" asked Sundiata.

"You will leave that to me," answered Bala Fasseke. "I shall uncover the secret of Sumanguru's weakness and return to you. In the meantime, form your army."

Thus the friends parted once more and Sundiata began to build his army. And at each town where Sundiata went, the princes gave him troops because of their hatred of Sumanguru and their love of Sundiata.

So in this time Sundiata left his mother who was ugly. Yet she was beautiful, and loved her son, and had suffered. Truly the love of a mother and a sister are deeper than a man can understand.

Book 10

Sumanguru brooded in the silence of his tower. All evening he had listened to the music of the djinns. Their music was like the sound of flies, a buzzing, droning whine above which their voices floated in chants older than this world.

But Sumanguru had grown weary of it and had sent them away. Now, as he sat alone, he heard another music drifting up to the tower from the streets of Sosso. Someone was singing a song in praise of Sumanguru's sorcery. The words flowed like liquid gold, like fire, like an endless river. So Sumanguru descended from his tower and crossed the streets until he came upon a young man, dressed in rags, who sang among the people of Sosso.

"Begone, wretches," Sumanguru ordered his people and they fled away into their houses.

"Who are you, singer?" he asked the young man.

"I am called Bala Fasseke," was the answer. "I have heard men speak of you in all the regions of this land, saying that you are the master of all nations and the equal of Alexander the Great. Therefore I have come to sing your praises."

Sumanguru was pleased by these words and Bala Fasseke burst into a new song of such praise for the sorcerer that Sumanguru smiled.

"Can you play the bafalon?" he asked as Bala Fasseke finished his song. "I have a bafalon, there, in the tower, which was the gift of great djinns, a magical bafalon whose tone is as pure as the sun."

"Lead me, O Great Master, Lord of Lords, Terror of Enemies."

Soon they were in the chamber whose mats were the skins of dead kings. But Bala Fasseke took no notice of them and instead picked up the wooden mallets and began to play the bafalon of the djinns. And Sumanguru sat back in rapture as Bala Fasseke composed song after song in praise of the Sorcerer King.

Then abruptly, Bala Fasseke ceased playing.

"Go on. Go on, Bala Fasseke," urged Sumanguru.

"I cannot," answered the griot. He flung the wooden

mallets down and plunged his face into his hands.

"What is the matter?" cried Sumanguru, stunned by the strange behavior of the singer.

"O Great King, I dare not play longer. For I now remember that all great sorcerers have a taboo—some act, some word—which can destroy them."

"What of it? It need not concern you. Play on, singer."

"O Destroyer of All Foes, what if I should utter that word or commit that deed without knowing it, thus destroying the very being whose greatness is the source of my song and my joy?"

"It has nothing to do with singing. Sing on."

"Nay, I cannot, from fear of uttering that word or committing that deed."

"Play or die," snarled Sumanguru.

"I will not play. I cannot play. The words catch in my throat. My fingers tremble as they hold the mallets."

And this and much more did Bala Fasseke utter, but not one more note would he strike, not one more word would he sing, until Sumanguru cried out, "Sing, fool. My taboo is the rooster's spur. That is the thing I must fear, and not music."

And now Bala Fasseke began to sing again, and he played the bafalon more beautifully, more joyously than before. And when Sumanguru fell asleep among his mats of skin, Bala Fasseke left the tower of Sosso and set out across the grasslands.

Book 11

Who can number the men and the tribes that came to stand by the side of Sundiata? All cities flung open their gates at the approach of that great prince and the banners flew proudly. As the streams collect together and become a river, and the rivers collect together to become the sea, so the army of Sundiata grew. Across the Valley of the Serpent and down the course of the Bafing River, Sundiata's army moved, and the plains were black with men, the skies thick with dust.

Now Sumanguru heard of the return of Sundiata and remembered the words of the afreet who had read the cowrie shells, saying, "One of twelve shall defeat you in battle." Thus, in great terror, the sorcerer of Sosso as-

sembled an army of his own and sought to block the advance of Sundiata, who was driving down toward Tabon.

Sosso Bala, the son of Sumanguru, took charge of that army and waited in the valley to the north of Tabon so that Sundiata might not join forces with the King of Tabon.

And there the two armies met for the first time. But the son of Sumanguru was no match for the terrible Sundiata, whose cavalry was skilled in the techniques of the Arab warriors. Within two hours the field of battle was littered with the dead warriors of Sosso Bala. Riderless horses wandered among spent arrows and broken spears, and drank thirstily from blood-red streams.

The road to Tabon was open.

After that day many great battles were fought. Many brave men fell on both sides. Many cities burned to ashes. Many dreams died. And still Sumanguru kept the main body of his forces away from the army of Sundiata, until men began to desert from his side. Then he knew he must stand or die.

North of Koulikoro stands the town of Krina. The land is gentle, and the people also. Here Sumanguru determined to make his stand and defend the road to Sosso, with the Niger River upon his left, the rolling hills to his right, and the gorges of Koulikoro to the south.

For many days he prepared his troops as a great cloud

of dust far over the horizon, the army of Sundiata, approached relentlessly.

Then, on the day before the battle, Sumanguru rode across the fields by the side of Sosso Bala. "Do you see that mountain of stone to the southwest?" he said. "You will send warriors there, for it will make an excellent lookout."

"That is no mountain, Father, but the army of Sundiata, which is advancing upon us," answered his son.

"The mountain . . . the moving mountain. I remember the moving mountain. I remember the afreet who cast the shells, saying, 'When the mountain moves against you, Sosso shall fall in ruins.' "

Now Sumanguru looked into the pale sky and he did not move and his arms hung down by his sides. Then silently he wheeled his horse away and went up on a hill. There he stood and watched the mountain of stone all that day until the sun set.

* * * * *

They say, O children of Mali, that when the two armies met, a shudder swept throughout the whole of Africa and the pillars of the sky shook within their foundations.

Sumanguru called upon the winds, the rain, and the earthquake. Men died like insects. Banners fell under the trampling hoofs of a thousand horses. Whole tribes were massacred in a single charge and forests were leveled into fields. Never had men fought so savagely nor so long.

What began at dawn was raging as the sun began to set. Men no longer ran across the solid earth but over the bodies of the fallen.

And then, as the last rays of the setting sun touched the gently rolling hills of Krina, land of the gentle people, Sundiata sought out Sumanguru and found him.

The two men faced each other across the field of death. What vision passed across the eyes of the Sorcerer King at that moment when gently he said, "You have fought well, Sundiata"? Then, as the clouds pass by the sun, to reveal once again the terrible fire of heaven, the face of Sumanguru twisted and he drew his spear.

Sundiata drew back his bow, and the point of his arrow glittered in the light of the setting sun. Farakurun had prepared that arrow of wood and iron and the tip of the arrow was the spur of a rooster. Sundiata let it fly and it struck Sumanguru in the shoulder. For one brief moment, Sumanguru stared in horror at the arrow biting into his flesh. Then he tore it out and looked at the tip, the rooster's spur.

His magic ended then. The wind no longer obeyed him, nor the rains. And now Sundiata drew his curved sword and drove his horse forward. Sumanguru turned with a scream of rage and fled across the plains, deserting his son and his army. And they died, man by man and tribe by tribe.

For two days and two nights the chase continued. And on the evening of the third night, Sumanguru's horse died of exhaustion among the gorges of Koulikoro.

Behind him, the sorcerer could hear the hoofs of Sundiata's horse rushing down upon him. So he stood, finally, with his back against the canyon wall and drew his sword.

He waited while above him, from the region of the sandstone mountains, the owls came and perched among the leafless trees of the canyon. Then the earth shook and the wall of the canyon opened like some vast door, and Sumanguru turned and looked into a black and endless cavern which stretched on forever into the bowels of the earth.

And at the edge of the cavern, in the dust of the land, appeared a large, gray stone. A twisted arm stretched up from the gray mass, and two eyes, rimmed in red, opened and fixed upon the face of Sumanguru.

"Come, mighty simbon," said the dwarf and beckoned Sumanguru into the cave.

"Sumanguru!" cried Sundiata from behind.

"Enter, Sumanguru," said the dwarf and then he laughed.

"You knew all this would come to pass," muttered Sumanguru to the dwarf. "You knew."

"Sumanguru," cried Sundiata once more, and with a terrible cry of rage and horror, Sumanguru flung himself into the cave. And the mountain shut behind him.

* * * * *

So did Sundiata return alone to the world of men, and build a great empire, but Sumanguru vanished forever into the region of the kingdom of the dwarf.

About the Author

Roland Bertol first learned of the legend of Sundiata a number of years ago when he was preparing for a trip to Mali with a Norwegian film company. The company was to make a full-length feature film in and around Bamako, the capital city of Mali, and even though Mr. Bertol had lived in North Africa, he felt he knew almost nothing about Africa south of the Sahara. He began to read, and in the works of French and Arab historians he discovered for the first time the Africa of great empires. Almost by accident he stumbled onto the Sundiata.

"The Sundiata," Mr. Bertol says, "represents only a fraction of what Africa has to offer the world. Recently it has become popular to talk about 'Africa waking up.' That is true, but I think that something more important is taking place: we in the West are waking up to Africa."

Mr. Bertol was educated in France and America and has been a teacher in grammar school, high school, and college. He is the author of *The Two Hats: A Story of Portugal,* published in 1969.

About the Artist

Gregorio Prestopino's paintings have been exhibited at numerous museums, universities, and one-man shows throughout the United States. His work appears in many permanent collections including those of the Whitney Museum and the Museum of Modern Art in New York City, the Chicago Art Institute, the Smithsonian Institution, and the National Institute of Arts and Letters.

Mr. Prestopino was born and educated in New York City. He is the recipient of a number of prizes including a grant from the National Institute of Arts and Letters. Mr. Prestopino taught painting and drawing at the Museum of Modern Art, the Brooklyn Museum, and the New School. During 1968-69, he served as painter-in-residence at the American Academy in Rome.